I Spy Book for Toddlers
Transport Vehicles and Things That Go

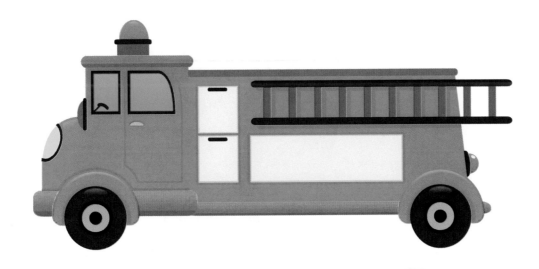

I Spy With My Little Eye Guessing Book
for Preschoolers - Ages 2-5

SMART BOOKS HUB

This book belongs to:

_____

I spy with my little eye
Something beginning with

P is for police car

I spy with my little eye
Something beginning with

d is for

delivery van

I spy with my little eye
Something beginning with

r

is for

rocket

I spy with my little eye
Something beginning with

 is for

ambulance

I spy with my little eye
Something beginning with

t is for

tractor

I spy with my little eye
Something beginning with

C is for

cement mixer

I spy with my little eye
Something beginning with

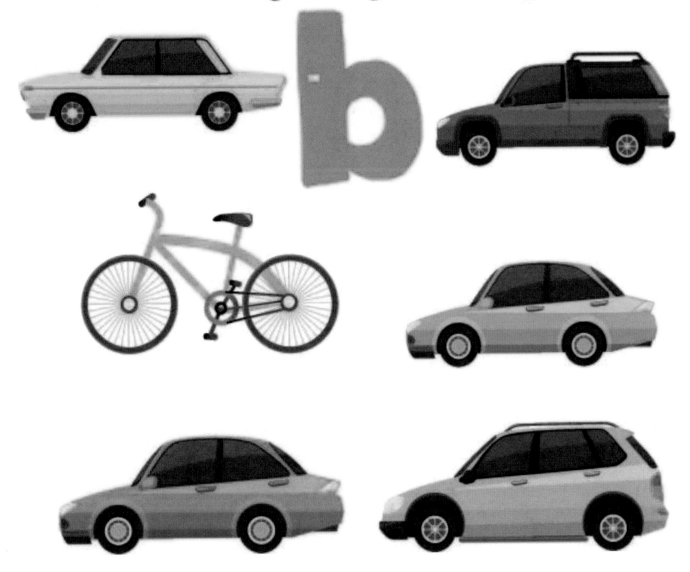

b is for

bicycle

I spy with my little eye
Something beginning with

a

is for

airplane

I spy with my little eye
Something beginning with

g is for

go kart

I spy with my little eye
Something beginning with

m is for

motor
cycle

S

is for

school bus

I spy with my little eye
Something beginning with

I spy with my little eye
Something beginning with

h is for

hot air
balloon

I spy with my little eye
Something beginning with

W is for

wagon

I spy with my little eye
Something beginning with

f is for

fire engine

I spy with my little eye
Something beginning with

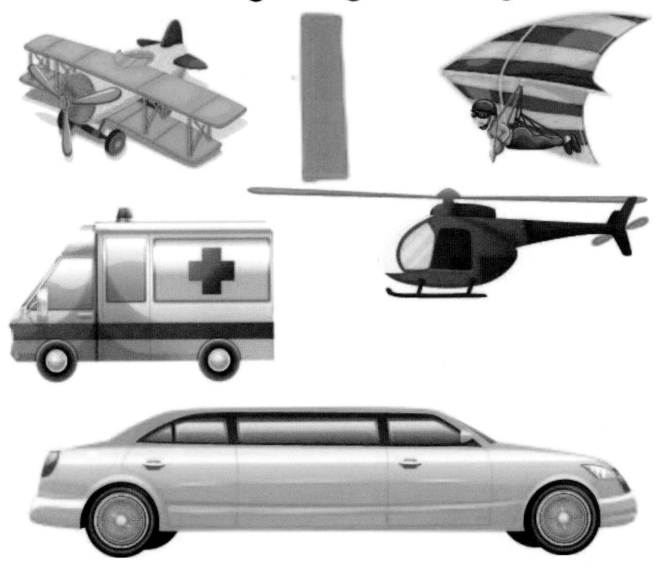

l is for

limousine

I spy with my little eye
Something beginning with

h
is for

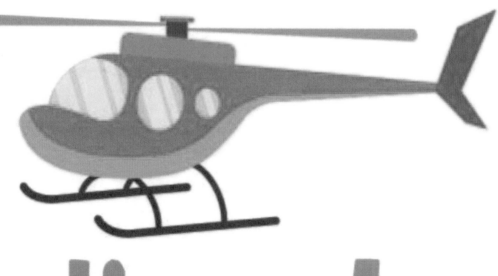

helicopter

I spy with my little eye
Something beginning with

V

is for

van

I spy with my little eye
Something beginning with

t is for

taxi

Made in the USA
Middletown, DE
22 December 2021